Planting a Rainbow

Written and illustrated by
Lois Ehlert

A TRUMPET CLUB SPECIAL EDITION

DEDICATED TO SHIRLEY AND DICK

Published by The Trumpet Club
666 Fifth Avenue, New York, New York 10103

ISBN 0-440-84713-3

This edition published by arrangement with
Harcourt Brace Jovanovich, Inc.
Printed in the United States of America
April 1992

10 9 8 7 6 5 4 3 2 1
UPR

Every year Mom and
I plant a rainbow.

In the fall we buy some bulbs

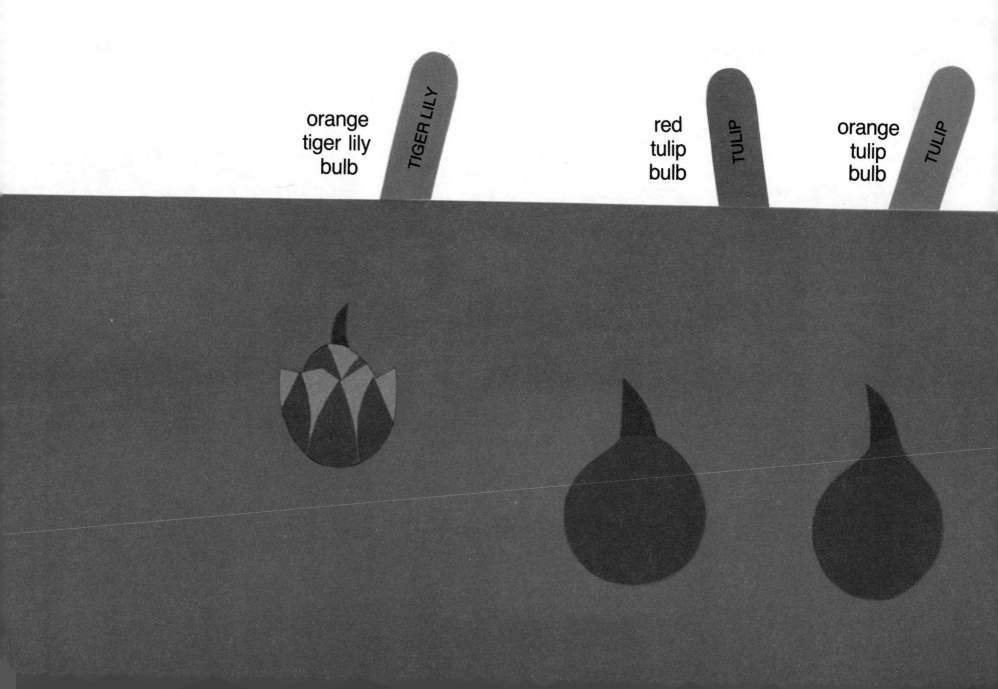

orange tiger lily bulb — TIGER LILY

red tulip bulb — TULIP

orange tulip bulb — TULIP

and plant them in the ground.

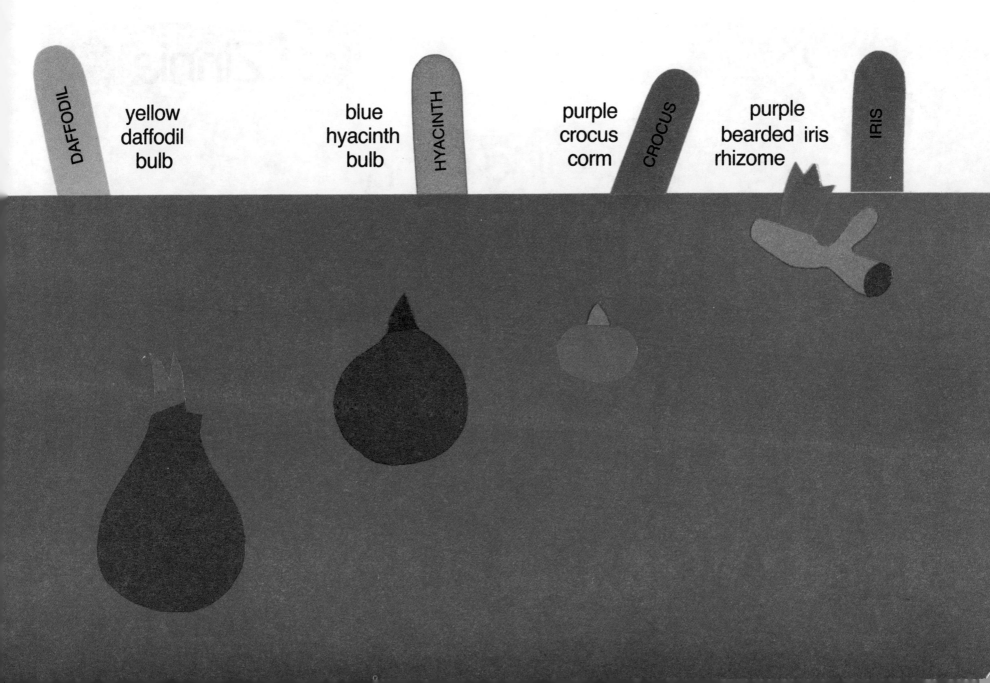

DAFFODIL

yellow
daffodil
bulb

blue
hyacinth
bulb

HYACINTH

purple
crocus
corm

CROCUS

purple
bearded iris
rhizome

IRIS

We order seeds from catalogs and

Phlox

Morning Glory

Zinnia

wait all winter long

Aster

Cornflower

Marigold

Daisy

for spring to warm the soil and sprout the bulbs.

TULIP

TULIP

DAFFODIL

HYACINTH

CROCUS

TULIP

TULIP

DAFFODIL

HYACINTH

CROCUS

Then it's time to go to the garden center to select some seedlings.

DELPHINIUM

POPPY

ROSE

We sow the seeds and set out the

TIGER LILY

DAISY

PHLOX

ASTER

CARNATION

ROSE

VIOLET

DELPHINIUM

plants in soil,

MARIGOLD

ZINNIA

MORNING GLORY

CORNFLOWER

IRIS

PANSY

POPPY

FERN

and watch the

TIGER LILY

DAISY

PHLOX

ASTER

CARNATION

ROSE

VIOLET

DELPHINIUM

rainbow grow,

MARIGOLD

ZINNIA

MORNING GLORY

CORNFLOWER

IRIS

PANSY

POPPY

FERN

and grow,

and grow.

tulips

carnations

We have some red flowers

rose

zinnia

and
orange
flowers,

tulip

poppy

tiger lily

and
some
yellow
blooms.

daisy

marigold

daffodils

We grow something green

ferns

and
some blue
flowers,

morning
glories

delphinium

hyacinth

cornflowers

and some
purple
flowers,
too.

phlox

crocus

iris

violets

asters

pansy

All summer long
we pick them
and bring them home.

And when summer is over,
we know we can grow our
rainbow again next year.